Life at McPherson

By John McPherson

McPherson Goes to Work
McPherson's Marriage Album
Life at McPherson High
McPherson's Sport & Fitness Manual*
McPherson on Parenting*
High School Isn't Pretty*

Published by HarperPaperbacks

*coming soon

LIFE AT
McPHERSON HIGH

JOHN McPHERSON

ZondervanPublishingHouse
HarperPaperbacks
Divisions of HarperCollins*Publishers*

This is a work of fiction. The characters, incidents, and dialogues are products of the author's imagination and are not to be construed as real. Any resemblance to actual events or persons, living or dead, is entirely coincidental.

HarperPaperbacks   *A Division of* HarperCollins*Publishers*
10 East 53rd Street, New York, N.Y. 10022

A trade paperback edition of this book was published in 1991 by ZondervanPublishingHouse, a *Division of* HarperCollins*Publishers*.

Cover illustration by John McPherson

First HarperPaperbacks printing: June 1995

Printed in the United States of America

HarperPaperbacks and colophon are trademarks of HarperCollins*Publishers*

10 9 8 7 6 5 4 3 2 1

For Mom and Dad

Special thanks to Chris Lutes without whose encouragement, editorial wisdom, and laughter this book would never have made it off the drawing board.

CLASSES

AS SOON AS HIS DAD BOUGHT THE VIDEO CAMERA, ERIC KNEW THAT THE FIRST DAY OF SCHOOL WOULD BE A CATASTROPHE.

MRS. MUTNER WENT OVER A FEW OF HER RULES ON THE
FIRST DAY OF SCHOOL.

JIM SCHAAD WAS ONE OF THE FEW PEOPLE IN THE
SCHOOL WHO COULD BURP THE ENTIRE
STAR TREK THEME SONG.

STUDENTS AT LIFFNER HIGH WERE SORT OF LET DOWN WHEN THEY FOUND OUT THAT THEIR FOREIGN EXCHANGE STUDENT WAS FROM OHIO.

"EXCUSE ME, MRS. NELTIK. WE HAD A BIOLOGY PROJECT GET A LITTLE OUT OF CONTROL NEXT DOOR. DID YOU BY ANY CHANCE SEE A GREEN AND RED SNAKE, ABOUT 6 OR 7 FEET LONG...OH, THERE HE IS!"

THIS WAS THE THIRD TIME IN A WEEK
THAT GREG GOT CAUGHT PASSING NOTES TO LIZ.

LYLE'S ABILITY TO TIE FLIES TO
LINDA SANDUSKY'S HAIR EARNED HIM
37 WEEKS OF DETENTION STUDY HALL.

BIOLOGY LAB

"SO, HOW WAS CHEM LAB?"

"EXCUSE ME, MR. NURMOND? CAN I TALK TO YOU ABOUT A LITTLE PROBLEM I RAN INTO ON MY BIOLOGY PROJECT?"

"BEFORE WE BEGIN TODAY'S DISSECTION LAB, I'D LIKE YOU EACH TO SELECT YOUR SPECIMEN AND TAKE IT BACK TO YOUR LAB TABLE."

"YOU'RE RIGHT! IT DOES LOOK LIKE PETE CLARK!"

MICROBIOLOGY
MR. LURWAD

McPHERSON

"THIS ISN'T WHAT I HAD IN MIND WHEN I SIGNED UP FOR SHOP CLASS."

KELLY BOWMAN'S TECHNIQUE FOR LATE PAPER EXCUSES WAS TO BABBLE INCESSANTLY UNTIL THE TEACHER GAVE IN.

WALT MESSES UP HIS RIGHT TURN SIGNAL ONCE AGAIN.

"BOY, THAT WAS SOME POTHOLE!"

RECENT BUDGET CUTS HAD MADE A DRASTIC EFFECT ON THE MEEKER HIGH DRIVER ED. PROGRAM.

STUDY TIP: SAVE TIME ON BIG READING ASSIGNMENTS BY READING EVERY OTHER WORD.

LET'S FACE IT. EVERYBODY DOES THIS WHEN THEY'RE ASSIGNED A 2000-WORD ESSAY.

THE MAGNA
CARTA WAS SIGNED IN
1215.

McPHERSON

WAYNE MERLMAN COULDN'T FIND A HI-LIGHTER, SO HE USED
A BLACK MAGIC MARKER TO CROSS OUT ALL THE STUFF HE DIDN'T
WANT TO READ AGAIN.

TEACHERS

NO PASSING ZONE

McPHERSON

LORETTA WAS STARTING TO THINK THAT
BEING THE TEACHER'S PET WASN'T ALL
IT WAS CRACKED UP TO BE.

IT DIDN'T TAKE MUCH TO UPSET MRS. BURNSNARD.

MRS. MORTLEMAN MADE SURE THAT EVERYONE PARTICIPATED IN CLASS.

CHRIS JUDD WILL KNOW BETTER THAN TO RAISE HIS HAND THE NEXT TIME MR. NORWOOD ASKED FOR A VOLUNTEER TO ERASE THE BLACKBOARD.

MR. GLEMPLY WAS A MASTER OF REVERSE PSYCHOLOGY.

NUMBER FOUR, CAN YOU ANSWER THAT QUESTION FOR US?

MR. GICKMAN WASN'T TOO GOOD WITH NAMES.

IT WASN'T LONG BEFORE STUDENTS STARTED TO TAKE ADVANTAGE OF MRS. GRINDLE'S NEARSIGHTEDNESS.

TWENTY YEARS OF INHALING FORMALDEHYDE FUMES
FINALLY CAUGHT UP WITH
BIOLOGY TEACHER RUTH MULDOON.

"SO, ANYWAY, RHONDA TOLD DORIS ALL ABOUT WAYNE AND...."

OUT IN THE HALLS

SEVERAL STUDENTS HAD THREATENED TO QUIT UNLESS
THE PRINCIPAL DROPPED HIS NEW DRESS CODE POLICY.

GOING TO THE SAME SCHOOL AS YOUR YOUNGER BROTHER CAN BE AN AGONIZING EXPERIENCE.

"I'M TRYING TO AVOID BEING ASSOCIATED WITH ANY ONE PARTICULAR PEER GROUP."

"HEY, KEITH, IS WHAT I HEARD TRUE?
DID GARY SLATER REALLY STUFF YOU INTO
YOUR LOCKER AND LEAVE YOU THERE FOR 5 HOURS?"

WILL'S NEW HABIT OF WEARING BOWLING SHOES
TO SCHOOL WAS HAVING A NEGATIVE EFFECT ON
HIS SOCIAL LIFE.

SPROING!

BOING!

McPherson

ONE OF THE HOTTEST FADS EVER TO HIT
BIMSLEY HIGH: TRAMPOLINE SHOES.

MIKE OHLER WAS SICK AND TIRED OF
FORGETTING HIS LOCKER COMBINATION.

EXAMS

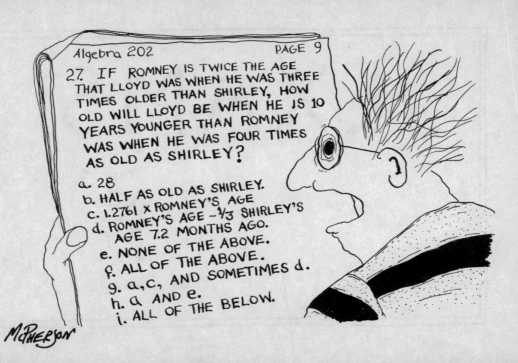

"LEON! KEEP YOUR EYES ON YOUR OWN PAPER!!"

EVERY HIGH SCHOOL STUDENT'S WORST ENEMY:
THE ESSAY QUESTION.

MRS. BRADT HOPED THAT ORAL MIDTERMS IN SPANISH 201
WOULD GIVE STUDENTS A UNIQUE CULTURAL EXPERIENCE.

MORE AND MORE STUDENTS ARE RELYING ON PRIVATE COACHING FIRMS TO HELP THEM SCORE HIGHER ON THE SATS.

AN S.A.T. SAMPLE QUESTION IS USED TO TEST STUDENTS' SENSE OF LOGIC.

SIX EXAMS IN 2½ DAYS HAD TAKEN THEIR TOLL ON PHIL WOGNARZ.

STUDY TIP: IF YOU'RE TAKING A COMPUTER SCORED TEST, BUT FORGOT TO BRING A NO. 2 PENCIL, USE TWO NO. 1 PENCILS INSTEAD.

S.A.T. PROCTORS ARE SPECIALLY TRAINED TO TERRORIZE STUDENTS BY CONTINUOUSLY WRITING DOWN THE TIME LEFT IN THE EXAM.

OUT TO LUNCH

"I HATE IT WHEN THE TRACK TEAM COMES TO LUNCH."

"DOES ANYBODY WANT THE REST OF MY
PEANUT BUTTER, MUSTARD, AND ASPARAGUS SANDWICH?"

"GARCÓN!"

NEEDLESS TO SAY, 98% OF THE STUDENTS AT MILPOT HIGH BROUGHT THEIR OWN LUNCHES.

IT WAS ABOUT TIME SOMEBODY PUT UP SOME NO-PEST STRIPS IN THE THATCHER HIGH CAFETERIA.

RUMOR HAD IT THAT THERE WAS GOING TO BE A MASSIVE
FOOD FIGHT DURING 6TH PERIOD LUNCH.

RANGE, 12 FEET.

DAVE'S LATEST METAL SHOP PROJECT REVOLUTIONIZED FOOD FIGHTS.

EXTRACURRICULAR ACTIVITIES

GET INVOLVED!
JOIN A CLUB!

- YAHTZEE CLUB
- FUTURE JANITORS OF AMERICA
- LIMBO DANCERS' CLUB
- TAG TEAM TETHERBALL
- FUN WITH LOGARITHMS
- STUDENTS FOR BETTER EYEGLASS CARE.
- CALCULATOR REPAIR AND MAINTENANCE
- STUDENTS AGAINST BAD BREATH

McPHERSON

DESPERATE TO SELL MORE PAPERS, THE NEWSPAPER STAFF AT LUTNER HIGH STOOPS TO THE LOWEST FORM OF JOURNALISM.

LEO HAMBO   BARB HERD   MORT   DAVE HITCHCOCK   SUEHOOP ER   LIZ

McPHERSON

NOBODY WAS TOO PLEASED WITH THE
YEARBOOK STAFF AT WHATNEY HIGH.

"VERY GOOD, KATHY. THAT IS THE CORRECT SPELLING OF 'CARROT.' DON, WOULD YOU PLEASE SPELL 'PSEUDOPARENCHYMA.'"

LEON WAGGETT'S CHANCES OF WINNING THE
SCIENCE FAIR WERE LOOKING PRETTY SLIM.

UNABLE TO RAISE ENOUGH MONEY FOR A TEN-DAY TRIP TO PARIS, THE MUCKLER HIGH FRENCH CLUB HAD TO SETTLE FOR THREE DAYS IN CLEVELAND.

THE NUMBER-ONE ALL-TIME STUPIDEST SONG TO REQUEST AT A HIGH-SCHOOL DANCE.

THE LATEST IN STEREO TECHNOLOGY:
THE PARTY WALKMAN.

AN EARLY VERSION OF THE WALKMAN.

P. E.

DEEP DOWN INSIDE, COACH KNOTT HAD
ALWAYS WANTED TO BE A MATH TEACHER.

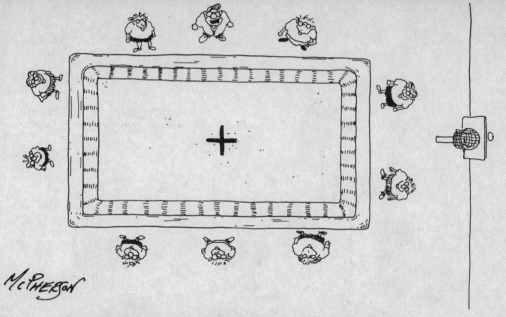

McPHERSON

"LET GO OF THE CEILING, WILKINS!"

YOU HEARD ME, LUPNER. NO HANDS OR FEET ALLOWED!

HOW TO TELL WHEN IT'S TIME TO CHANGE YOUR GYM SOCKS.

LLOYD USES A POWERFUL SELF-DEFENSE TECHNIQUE.

JOCKS

THE ATHLETIC PROGRAM AT MILFOIL HIGH
NEEDED SOME SERIOUS UPGRADING.

"COACH SAYS NEXT YEAR WE'LL HAVE ENOUGH MONEY TO GET REAL HELMETS."

"IF YOU WANT MY OPINION, I THINK OUR COLOR GUARD IS OUT TO LUNCH."

DUE TO RECENT BUDGET CUTS, ROBERSON HIGH WAS
FORCED TO COMBINE ITS CROSS COUNTRY AND ARCHERY PROGRAMS.

TRACK COACH WALT SPUZMAN WAS KNOWN FOR HIS HARSH TRAINING METHODS.

BEING A CHEERLEADER FOR THE CROSS-COUNTRY
TEAM WAS NOT AN EASY TASK.

THUNK!

NEXT YEAR THE TEAM HOPED TO BUY OFFICIAL BACKBOARDS.

MORALE ON THE WADLEY HIGH BASKETBALL TEAM
STARTED TO SLIP DURING THE PRE-GAME MEETING.

THE SMELDNER HIGH CHEERLEADERS DID LITTLE
TO BOOST THE TEAM'S MORALE.

IT WAS SOMETIME DURING THE THIRD PERIOD
THAT THE WEEDMONT HIGH CHEERLEADERS
TURNED ON THEIR OWN TEAM.

WALT OWED THIS VICTORY TO 10 YEARS OF BOY SCOUT TRAINING.

AS MEMBERS OF THE BOWLING TEAM, THE ROBB BROTHERS KNEW THIS WAS A ONCE IN A LIFETIME OPPORTUNITY.

SOMEBODY SABOTAGED THE FERBERVILLE
HIGH 440-RELAY TEAM BY PUTTING
SUPER-GLUE ON THEIR BATON.

THE HIGH HURDLES WERE NOT GLENN'S STRONGEST EVENT.

"THIS NEW TRAINING METHOD HAS INCREASED THEIR JUMPS BY 70%."

NO ONE COULD SLIDE LIKE JUSTIN "THE MOLE" FRAWLEY.

THE UMPIRES WERE STARTING TO SUSPECT THAT ZACK MIGHT BE THROWING A SPITBALL.

DATING

STELLA'S FATHER SHOULD HAVE KNOWN BETTER THAN TO ANSWER THE PHONE WHEN SHE WAS HOPING FOR A CALL FROM POTENTIAL PROM DATES.

No, August is booked solid, September 6th is possible if you get me back by 6. There might be some openings in late October. Cancellations? No chance!

McPHERSON

NEEDLESS TO SAY, CHUCK'S SERENADING DIDN'T GET HIM A DATE WITH JEANNIE.

"LOOK, I KNOW THIS WAS A REALLY WEIRD THING TO DO BUT I DIDN'T KNOW HOW ELSE TO GET YOUR ATTENTION. ANYWAY, I WAS WONDERING IF YOU'D LIKE TO GO OUT FRIDAY NIGHT."

McPHERSON

JAMEE HAD MADE A SERIOUS SCHEDULING ERROR.

"PSST! MAKE SURE YOU GET HER HOME BY TWELVE."

McPHERSON

THE BLIND DATE THAT WAS DESTINED TO FAIL.

ANOTHER DATE RUINED BY AN
EMBARRASSING COMMERCIAL.

"SO, YOU'RE OFF TO THE
BIG PROM TONIGHT, EH?
WHOOPS! SORRY ABOUT THAT."

AS AN EXPRESSION OF HIS DEEP LOVE FOR HER,
DAVE MADE JAMEE A PROM DRESS IN WOODSHOP.

McPHERSON

AS ALWAYS, THE ANNUAL HIP-BOOT FORMAL AT MATTONE HIGH WAS A BIG SUCCESS.

"MOM! IT'S _NOT_ A _DATE!_ HE'S ONLY A _FRIEND._"

LOUISE WAS STARTING TO DROP SOME SUBTLE
HINTS THAT SHE DIDN'T WANT TO SEE VERN ANYMORE.

RATHER THAN LEAD WALT ON, LOIS THOUGHT IT BEST TO BE UP FRONT ABOUT HER DECISION TO BREAK UP WITH HIM.

THE HOLIDAYS

IT DIDN'T TAKE PEOPLE LONG TO DISCOVER THAT THE SMIDLEY HIGH CHRISTMAS COMMITTEE HAD MISTAKENLY DECKED THE HALLS WITH BOUGHS OF POISON IVY.

SAY! ISN'T THAT MISTLETOE?!

McPHERSON

SO FAR NO ONE HAD FALLEN FOR HOWARD MUSLAP'S MISTLETOE TRICK.

STUDENTS IN MR. MUSKIN'S MATH CLASS SUDDENLY
LOST THE SPIRIT OF CHRISTMAS WHEN THEY DISCOVERED
THAT THE GIFTS HE HAD GIVEN THEM CONTAINED
THEIR MIDTERM EXAMS.

LORETTA SLAGG, BURNFEST HIGH'S
VERSION OF THE GRINCH.

AAGH!

MRS. OXNARD'S END OF THE YEAR GIFT TO EVERYONE WHO PASSED
HER CLASS MADE MOST OF THEM WISH THEY HADN'T.

EVERYONE IN MRS. SNURLMAN'S CLASS PITCHED
IN AND GOT HER THE ULTIMATE GIFT:
A GAS-POWERED BLACKBOARD ERASER.

PARENTS

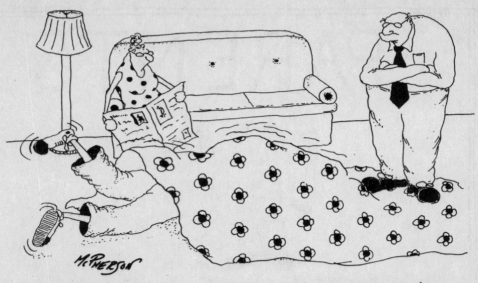

BOB TRIED IN VAIN TO GET THROUGH THE LIVING ROOM WITHOUT SHOWING HIS REPORT CARD TO HIS PARENTS.

AS PUNISHMENT FOR HIS LOW GRADES, WAYNE'S MOTHER FORCED HIM TO WATCH 12 HOURS OF HEE HAW RERUNS.

LORRAINE'S WORST NIGHTMARE COMES TRUE.

A CURFEW WAS NOT SOMETHING TO BE TAKEN LIGHTLY
IN THE MILLIGAN HOUSEHOLD.

"WALTER, WE WON'T HAVE TO BUY DOREEN A NEW PROM DRESS AFTER ALL. MY OLD PROM DRESS FITS HER PERFECTLY!"

MR. MELNIK EXPRESSES HIS DISAPPROVAL OF
WENDY'S NEW BOYFRIEND.

"LOOK, MOM AND DAD. ALL I WANT IS A LITTLE MORE INDEPENDENCE. IS THAT TOO MUCH TO ASK?"

WALLY NORTMAN WAS A MASTER AT
BEATING CURFEWS.

BOB'S NEW BUSINESS VENTURE WASN'T THE GOLD
MINE HE HAD THOUGHT IT WOULD BE.

TED'S CHANCES OF GETTING A RAISE
WEREN'T LOOKING TOO HOT.

★ TOP 5 SINGLES ★

1. WHOA, BABY, BABY, I LOVE YOU.
   BY WARY LILVIN.
2. YEAH, BABY, BABY, WHOA.
   BY THE MANDES
3. LOVE YOU BABY, WHOA, YEAH.
   BY THE SMNOELS
4. YEAH, YEAH, YEAH, BABY.
   BY RANDYS MOSWI.
5. BABY, BABY, LOVE YOU, YEAH, WHOA.
   BY LORMAN PRHAS.

RECORD HUT

TAPES   CDS
VIDEOS   ALBUMS

$11.46

McPHERSON

THURL'S WEED TRIMMING JOB AT MR. WIMPLE'S COMES TO AN ABRUPT HALT.

BRRAAAMM!!

BUD'S LAWN AND HAIR CARE

BUD FOUND A GREAT WAY TO EXPAND ON HIS SUMMER LAWN JOB.

GRADUATES

LOUIS WRZYNSKI'S LIFELONG FASCINATION
WITH DOMINOES CULMINATED IN THIS ONE FATEFUL MOMENT.

"I ALWAYS THOUGHT 'SHEEPSKIN' WAS JUST AN EXPRESSION."

"I DON'T HAVE TO RETURN THE CAP AND GOWN UNTIL WEDNESDAY, SO I FIGURED I MIGHT AS WELL GET SOME USE OUT OF THEM."

ENROLL NOW AT

ED'S UNIVERSITY!

- ONLY $700 PER SEMESTER!
- BUY 2 SEMESTERS, GET THE 3rd ONE AT HALF PRICE!

AND, IF YOU ORDER NOW, YOU'LL GET THE FOLLOWING COURSES ABSOLUTELY FREE!

1. COUNTING
2. INTERMEDIATE HAIRSTYLING
3. THE HISTORY OF BOWLING

STOP BY ED'S CAMPUS NOW AND RECEIVE A FREE ED'S U. TOTE BAG, NO PURCHASE NECESSARY!

* OFFER VOID WHERE PROHIBITED
* NOT AVAILABLE IN ANY STORES

ED MUTTLEY PRESIDENT

SUMMER
VACATION

THE DREADED END-OF-THE-YEAR LOCKER CLEAN-OUT.

McPHERSON

WITH SUMMER ON THE WAY, PEGGY WAS TRYING
DESPERATELY TO GET A HEAD START ON HER TAN.

"THE SEAT THAT CAME WITH THE BIKE WAS TOO DARNED UNCOMFORTABLE."

SUMMER WASN'T EVEN HALFWAY OVER, AND ALREADY THE DREADED SIGNS BEGAN TO APPEAR.

STUDENTS AT WAGNER HIGH WEREN'T READY TO
ACCEPT THE FACT THAT SUMMER VACATION WAS OVER.